Just Voices
Popular
Favourites

NOVELLO PUBLISHING LIMITED
part of The Music Sales Group
London / New York / Paris / Sydney / Copenhagen / Berlin / Madrid / Tokyo

Published by
Novello Publishing Limited
14-15 Berners Street, London, W1T 3LJ, UK.

Exclusive distributors:
Music Sales Limited
Distribution Centre, Newmarket Road,
Bury St Edmunds, Suffolk, IP33 3YB, UK.

Music Sales Pty Limited
120 Rothschild Avenue, Rosebery,
NSW 2018, Australia.

Order No. NOV940632
ISBN 13: 978-1-84609-875-8
ISBN 10: 1-84609-875-0

Edited by Rachel Payne.
Music processed by Paul Ewers Music Design.

Printed in the EU.

www.musicsales.com

Your Guarantee of Quality:
As publishers, we strive to produce every book
to the highest commercial standards.

The book has been carefully designed to
minimise awkward page turns and to make
playing from it a real pleasure.
Particular care has been given to specifying
acid-free, neutral-sized paper made from pulps
which have not been elemental chlorine bleached.

This pulp is from farmed sustainable forests
and was produced with special regard for
the environment.

Throughout, the printing and binding have
been planned to ensure a sturdy, attractive
publication which should give years of enjoyment.

If your copy fails to meet our high standards,
please inform us and we will gladly replace it.

Ain't No Sunshine 4

All I Have To Do Is Dream 8

Bridge Over Troubled Water 13

California Dreamin' 30

God Only Knows 18

I Say A Little Prayer 24

Our House 35

(Something Inside) So Strong 40

With A Little Help From My Friends 52

Yesterday Once More 46

Ain't No Sunshine

WORDS & MUSIC BY BILL WITHERS

long a-ny- time_ she goes a - way.
home an-ny- time_ she goes a - way.
home a-ny- time_ she goes a - way.

2. Won-der this_time where she's

do   do   do   do   do do   do do do

bom   bom bom   bom   bom bom bom

And I know, I know, I know,_ I know, I know, I know, I know,_ I know, I know, I

(like a high hat)

t t   t   t t   t   t t   t   t t   t

(finger snap)

bo   bo   bo   bo

know, I know, I know, I know, I know, I know, I know, I know, I know, I know, I know,

t   t   t   t   t   t   t   t   t   t   t

bo   bo   bo   bo

I know, I know, I know, I know, I know, I know, hey, I ought to leave the young thing a-

t   t   t   t   t   t   t   t   t   t   t   t

bo   bo   bo   bo

lone, but, ain't no sun-shine when she's gone._____ Ain't no sun-shine when she's

t t   t   do do   do do   do do   do do

bo   bo   bom   bom bom bom   bom bom

✠ *Coda*

A - ny - time_   she goes a - way.

do   do   do   do   do do   do do   do.

bom   bom bom   bom   bom bom   do.

All I Have To Do Is Dream

Words & Music by Boudleaux Bryant

I want you and all your charms, when ev-er I want you__ all I have to do is
I need you to hold me tight, when ev-er I want you__ all I have to do is

I want you and all your charms, when ev-er I want you all I have to do is
I need you to hold me tight, when ev-er I want you all I have to do is

I want you and all your charms, when ev-er I want you all I have to do is
I need you to hold me tight, when ev-er I want you all I have to do is

1.
dream,_____ dream, dream, dream. When
2.
dream._____

dream,_____ dream, dream, dream.When dream._____ Do do do do

dream,_____ dream, dream, dream.When dream._____ Do do do do do do do

9

I can make you mine, taste your lips of wine, a - ny time, night or day.

I can make you mine, taste your lips of wine, a - ny time, night or day. do do do

I can make you mine, taste your lips of wine, a - ny time, night or day. do do do

On - ly trou - ble is, gee whiz, I'm dream - ing my life__ a - way!_____ I

On - ly trou - ble is, gee whiz, I'm dream - ing my life a - way! I

On - ly trou - ble is, gee whiz, I'm dream - ing my life__ a - way!_____ I

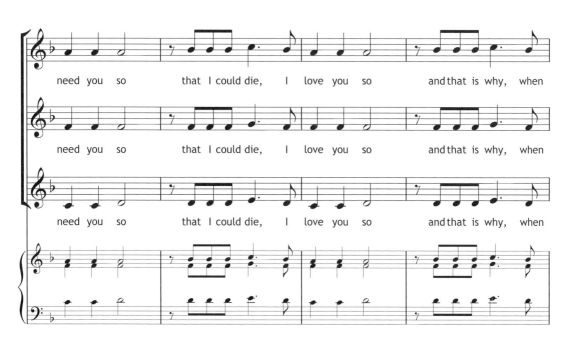

need you so   that I could die,   I love you so   and that is why, when

need you so   that I could die,   I love you so   and that is why, when

need you so   that I could die,   I love you so   and that is why, when

1.

ev - er I want you   all I have to do   is   dream.____

ev - er I want you   all I have to do   is   dream.____

ev - er I want you   all I have to do   is   dream.____

dream, dream, dream, dream,

Do do do do dream, dream, dream, dream,

Do do do do do do do dream, dream, dream, dream,

dream, dream, dream, dream, dream.

dream, dream, dream, dream, dream.

dream, dream, dream, dream, dream.

Bridge Over Troubled Water

Words & Music by Paul Simon

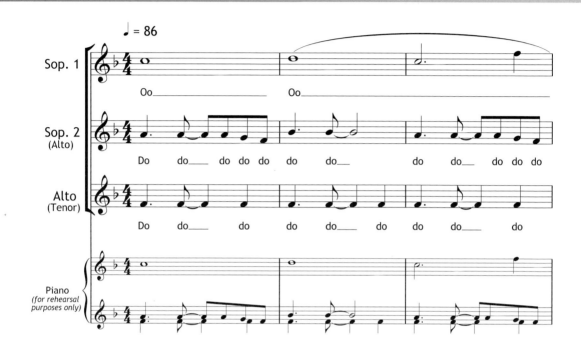

small,
street,
by.

when tears are in your eyes,
when eve - ning falls so hard
Your time has come to shine

do do do doo. When tears are in your eyes,
(2.) When eve - ning falls so hard
(3.) Your time has come to shine

do do do doo doo doo doo do do do

— I'll dry them all. Oo
— I'll com - fort you. Oo
— Your dreams are on their way,

— I'll dry them all.
— I'll com - fort you. } Do do do do do do
— Do do do do.

do do do do do do do do do do

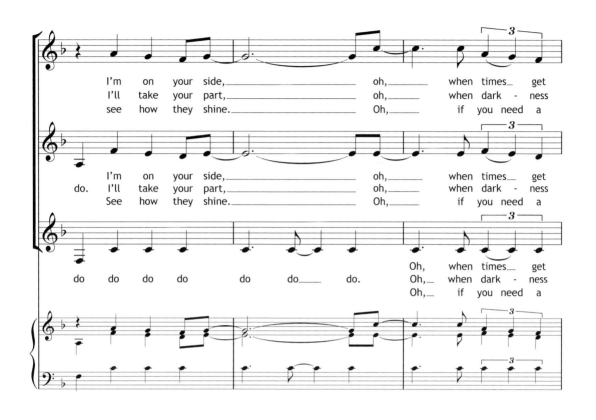

15

3rd time to Coda ⊕

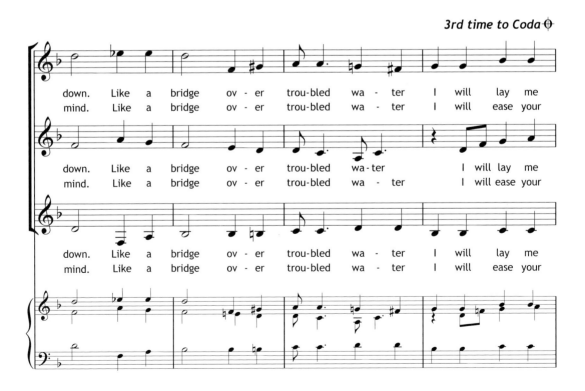

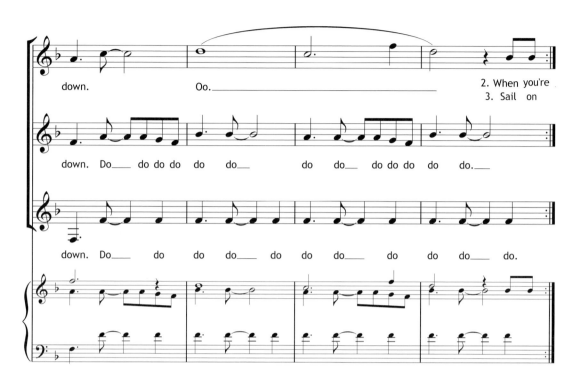

down.   Oo._____

2. When you're
3. Sail on

down. Do___ do do do do do___   do do___ do do do do do.___

down. Do___   do   do___ do do do___ do do do___ do.

$\oplus$ *Coda*

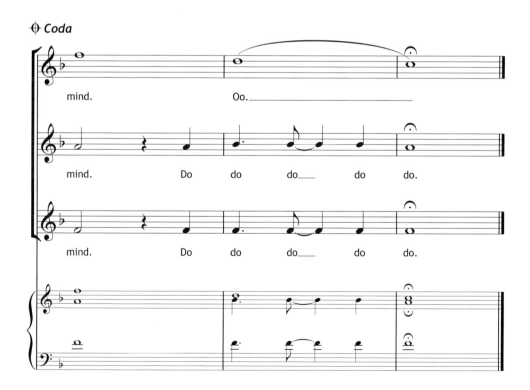

mind.   Oo._____

mind.   Do   do   do___ do do.

mind.   Do   do   do___ do do.

God Only Knows

Words & Music by Brian Wilson & Tony Asher

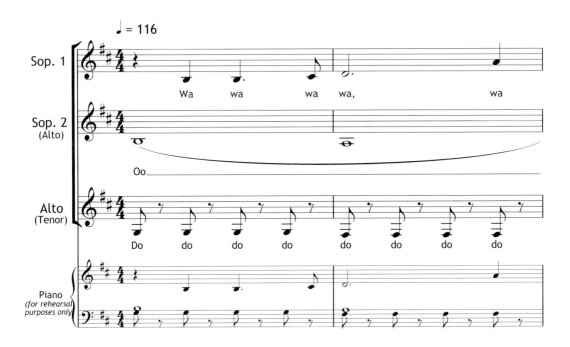

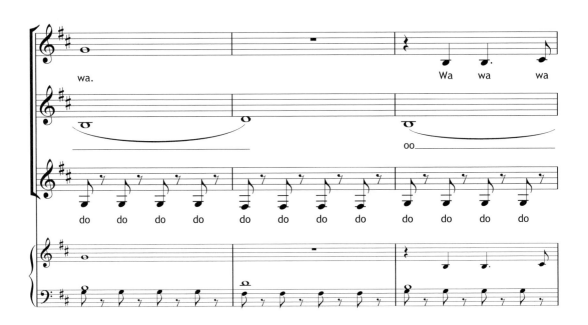

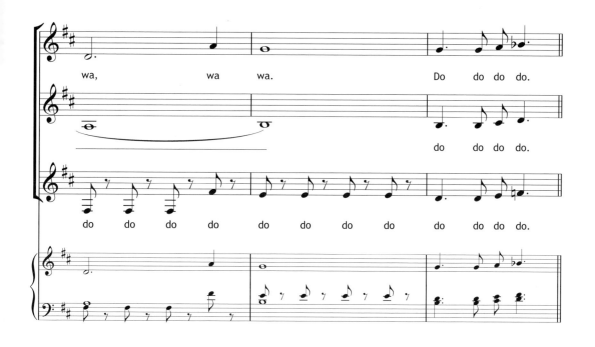

wa,   wa wa.   Do   do   do do.

do   do   do do.

do   do   do   do   do   do   do   do   do   do do do.

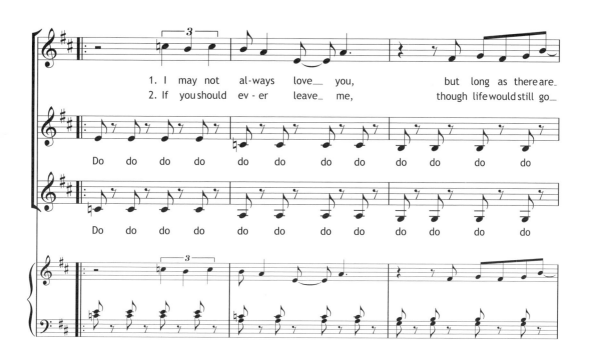

1. I may not al-ways love__ you,   but long as there are__
2. If you should ev - er leave__ me,   though life would still go__

Do   do   do   do   do   do   do   do   do   do   do

Do   do   do   do   do   do   do   do   do   do   do

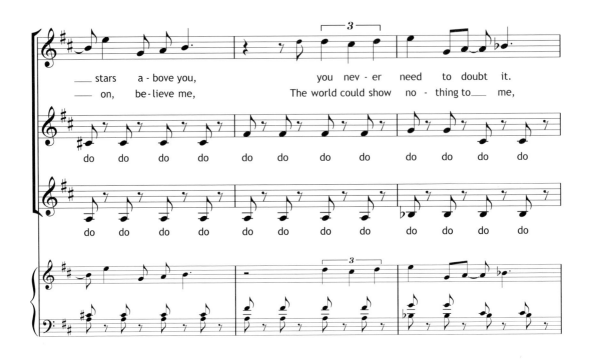

_____ stars a - bove you,
_____ on, be - lieve me,
you nev - er need to doubt it.
The world could show no - thing to_____ me,

do do do do do do do do do do do do

do do do do do do do do do do do do

I'll make you so_____ sure a - bout it.
So what good would_____ liv - ing do me?
God on - ly knows_____

do do do do do do do do do do do do

do do do do do do do do do do do do

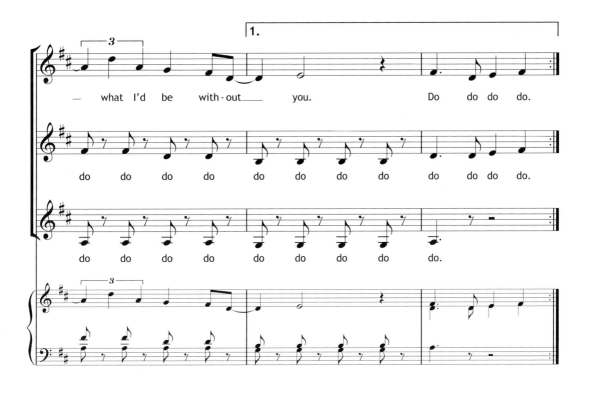

what I'd be with - out___ you. Do do do do.

do do do do do do do do do do do do.

do do do do do do do do do.

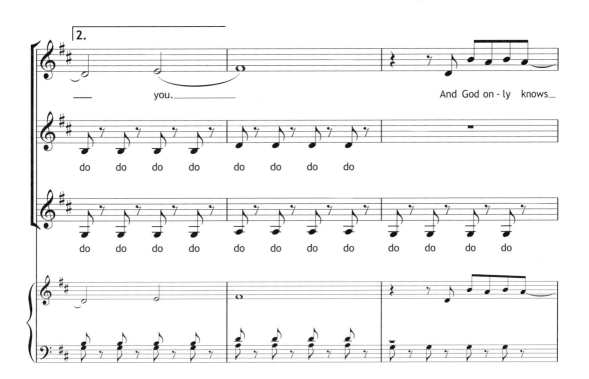

you.___ And God on - ly knows___

do do do do do do do do

do do do do do do do do do do do do

I Say A Little Prayer

WORDS BY HAL DAVID
MUSIC BY BURT BACHARACH

say a lit - tle prayer for you.___ While comb - ing my
say a lit - tle prayer for you.___ At work___ I just
say a lit - tle prayer for you.___
say a lit - tle prayer for you.___ do do___ do
say a lit - tle prayer for you.___ do___ do do do do___ do

hair now   and won - d'ring what dress___ to___
take time,   And all through my cof - fee___
do do___ do do do___ do do do
do do___ do do do___ do do do

wear now____ I say a lit-tle prayer for you.____ For-
break time____ I say a lit-tle prayer for you.____

do do__ do say a lit-tle prayer for you.____ For-

do do__ do say a lit-tle prayer for you.____ Oh._____ For-

-ev er, for-ev-er you'll stay in my heart__ and I will love you for-

-ev er, for-ev-er you'll stay in my heart__ and I will love you for-

-ev er, for-ev-er you'll stay in my heart__ and I will love you for-

ev-er and ev-er we nev-er will part,___ oh how I'll love you, to-

ev-er and ev-er we nev-er will part,___ oh how I'll love you, to-

ev-er and ev-er we nev-er will part,___ oh how I'll love you, to-

geth-er, to-geth-er, that's how it must be.___ To live with-out you would

geth-er, to-geth-er, that's how it must be.___ To live with-out you would

geth-er, to-geth-er, that's how it must be.___ To live with-out you would

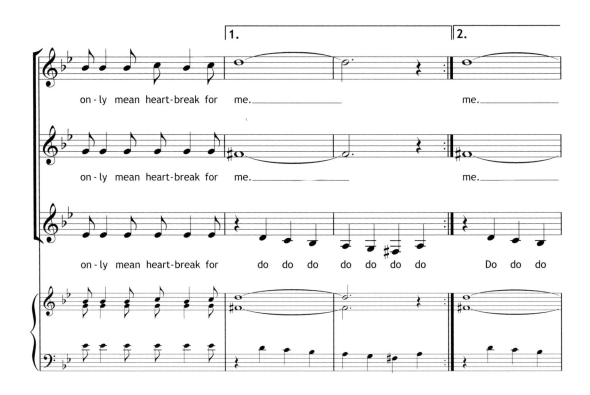

1. on-ly mean heart-break for me._____

2. me._____

on-ly mean heart-break for me._____ me._____

on-ly mean heart-break for do do do do do do do Do do do

_____ My darl - ing be - lieve me, for me___ there is

Do do___ do do do___ do do do___ do

do do do do do do___ do do do___ do do do___ do

no one_____ but you.   Say you love me

do   do___ do do do___ do   do do___ do do do___   do

do   do___ do do do___ do   do do___ do do do___   do

too._____   Say you love me   too._____

do   do___ do do do___   do   do._____

do   do___ do do do___   do   do._____

California Dreamin'

Words & Music by John Phillips & Michelle Phillips

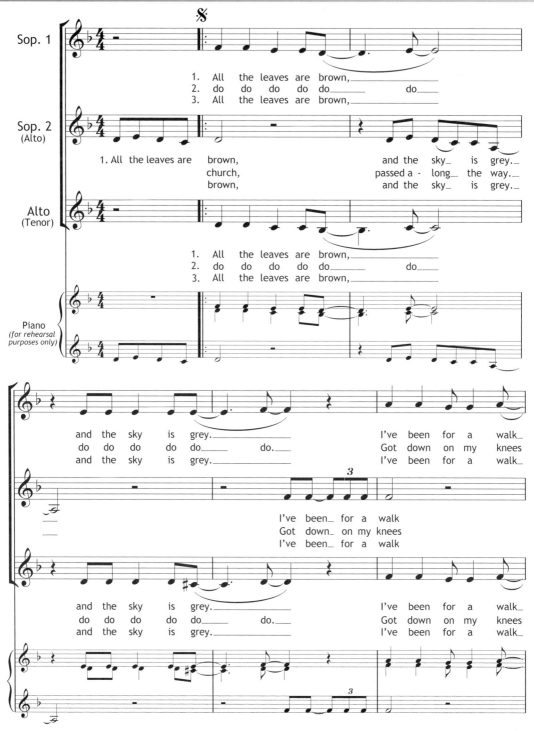

31

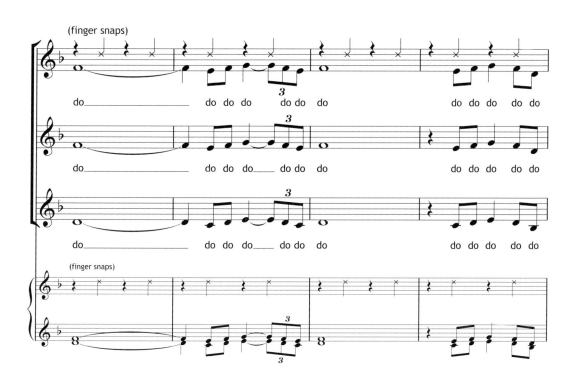

D.S. al Coda
(3rd Verse)

33

Coda

Cal - i - for - nia dream - in' on such a win-ter's day. Cal - i - for - nia dream

dream-in' on such a win-ter's day. Cal - i - for - nia dream

Cal - i - for - nia dream - in' on such a win-ter's day. Cal - i - for - nia dream

- in' on such a win-ter's day. Cal - i - for - nia dream - in' on such a win-ter's day.

- in' on such a win-ter's day. Cal - i - for - nia dream - in' on such a win-ter's day.

- in' on such a win-ter's day. Cal - i - for - nia dream - in' on such a win-ter's day.

Our House

WORDS & MUSIC BY GRAHAM NASH

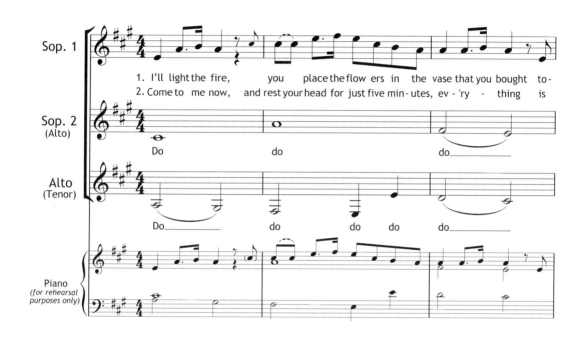

play your love songs all night long for me,_____ on - ly for me._____
sun - shine through them, fie - ry gems for you,_____ on - ly for you._____

play your love__ songs all night long__ for
(2.) sun - shine through them, fie - ry gems__ for

do do do do do do do do do do do do

play your love songs all night long for
(2.) sun - shine through them, fie - ry gems for

do_____ do do do

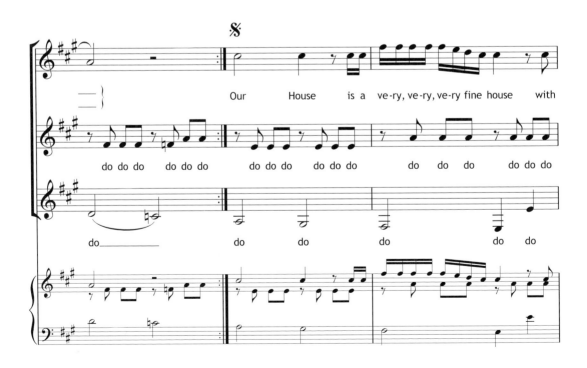

Our House is a ve - ry, ve - ry, ve - ry fine house with

do do do do do do do do do do do do do do do do do do

do_____ do do do do do

two cats in the yard, life used to be so hard,___ now ev - 'ry - thing is ea - sy 'cause of

do do do do do do do do do do do do do do do do do do

do do do do do do

⊕ To Coda

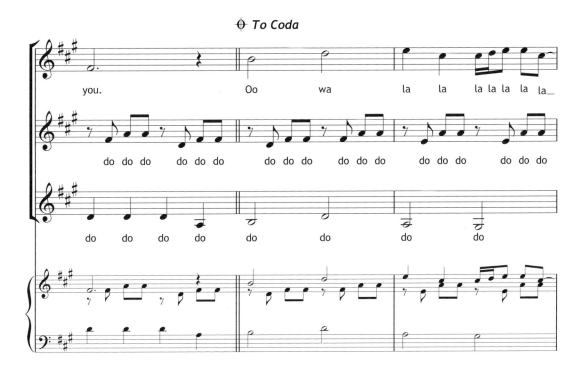

you. Oo wa la la la la la la la___

do do do do do do do do do do do do do do do do do do

do do do do do do do do

la la la la__ la la la la   la   la la la la__ la la la   la   la la la la la la la

do do do   do do do   do do do   do do do   do do do   do do do

do   do   do   do   do   do   do   do

D.S. al Coda

la   la   la la la la la__ la la la la__ la la la la   la   la la la la__ la la la

do do do   do do do   do do do   do do do   do do do   do do do

do   do   do do do   do   do

Coda

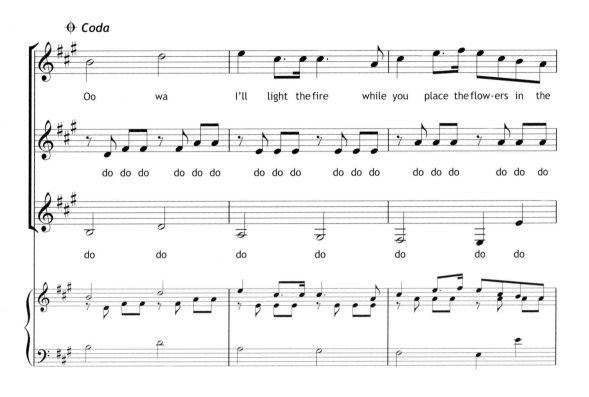

Oo wa I'll light the fire while you place the flow-ers in the

do do do do do do do do do do do do do do do do do do

do do do do do do do

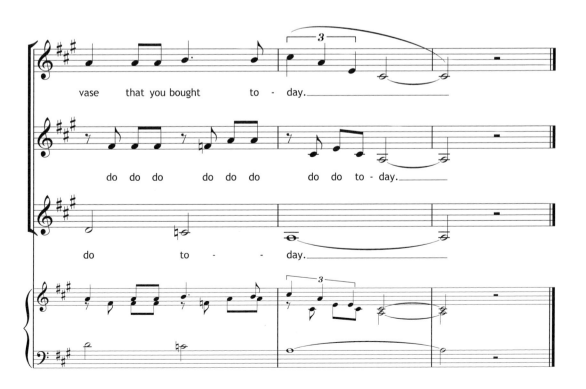

vase that you bought to - day.

do do do do do do do do to - day.

do to - - day.

(Something Inside) So Strong

WORDS & MUSIC BY LABI SIFFRE

do do___   do do___   do do___   do do_

do do___   do do___   do do___   do do_

way   the fast - er I will run.   You can de - ny me,
cho,   (your)lies will_ come tum - bl - ing.   De - ny my place in

do do___ do do___ do do___   do do___   do

do do___ do do___ do do___   do do___   do

you can de - cide   to turn your face_ a - way.___   No mat - ter 'cause there's
you squan - der wealth that's mine, my light_ will shine___   so bright - ly 'cause there's

some-thing in - side so strong._____ I

some-thing in - side so strong._____ I

some-thing in - side so strong._____ I

know that I___ can make it, though you're do - ing me wrong, so wrong.

know that I___ can make it, though you're do - ing me wrong, so wrong.

know that I___ can_ make it, though you're do - ing me wrong, so wrong.

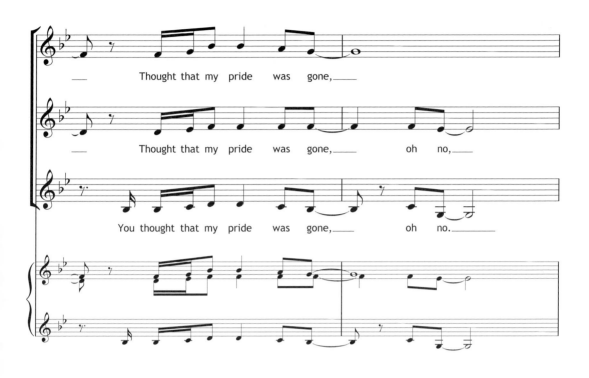

Thought that my pride was gone,____

Thought that my pride was gone,____ oh no,____

You thought that my pride was gone,____ oh no.____

some-thing in - side so strong.____ Oh,____

some-thing in - side so strong.____ Oh,____

There's some-thing in - side so strong.____ Oh,____

some-thing in - side so strong.___

some-thing in - side so strong.___

some-thing in - side so strong.___

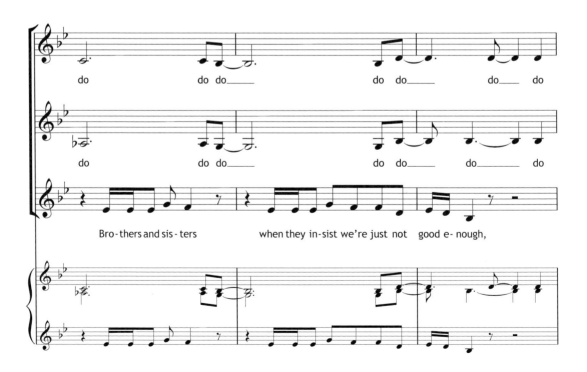

do   do do___   do do___   do___ do

do   do do___   do do___   do___ do

Bro - thers and sis - ters   when they in-sist we're just not good e- nough,

do do___ do do   do do___   do do__

do do_____ do do   do do___   do do_

when we know bet- ter,   just look 'em in the eyes and say

D.S. al Fine

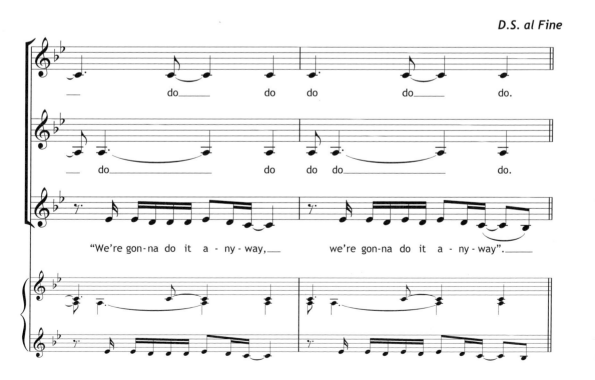

__ do_____ do do do_____ do.

__ do_____ do do do_____ do.

"We're gon-na do it a - ny - way,__   we're gon-na do it a - ny - way".__

Yesterday Once More

Words & Music by Richard Carpenter & John Bettis

1. When I was young I'd lis-ten to the ra-di-o__ wait-in' for my fa-'vrite songs.
(2.) back on how it was in years gone by,__ and the good times that I had,__

Do do do do do do
Do do do do do do

When they played I'd sing a-long,__ it made me smile.__
makes to-day seem ra-ther sad,__ so much has changed.__

do do do do do do do it made me,
do do do do do do do it made me,

Those were such hap-py times, and not so long a - go,___ how I
It was songs of love___ that I would sing to them,_ and I'd

made me smile._   Do   do   do   do

made me smile._   Do   do   do   do

won - dered where they'd gone,___ but they're back a - gain,_ just like a
me - mo - rise each word.___ Those old me - lo - dies_____ still sound so

do   do   do   do   do   doo - bee

do   do   do   do   do   doo - bee

long lost friend,__ all the songs I love so well.__ Ev - 'ry
good to me,__ as they melt the years a - way.__ Ev - 'ry

do doo - bee do doo - bee do. Ev - 'ry

do doo - bee do doo - bee do. Ev - 'ry

sha - la - la - la,__ ev - 'ry wo__ wo__ still shines.__

sha - la - la - la,__ wo wo__ sha - la - la - la,__ ev - 'ry

sha - la - la - la,__ wo wo__ sha - la - la - la,__ ev - 'ry

Ev -'ry shing-a-ling-a-ling that they're start-in' to sing___ so fine.

wo___ wo___ shing-a-ling-a-ling start-in' to sing___

wo___ wo___ shing-a-ling-a-ling start-in' to sing___

When they get to the part___ where he's
All my best me-mo-ries___ come back

start-in' to sing___ so fine___ do do

start-in' to sing___ so fine do do

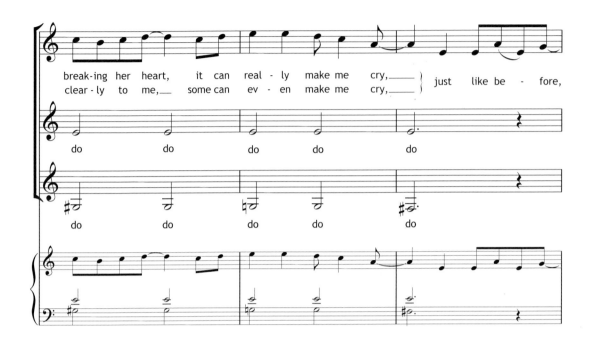

break-ing her heart, it can real - ly make me cry,____ just like be - fore,

clear - ly to me,___ some can ev - en make me cry,____ just like be - fore,

do   do   do   do   do

do   do   do   do   do

____ it's yes - ter - day once more.____

just like be - fore.____   shoo - bie do

just like be - fore.____   more.____

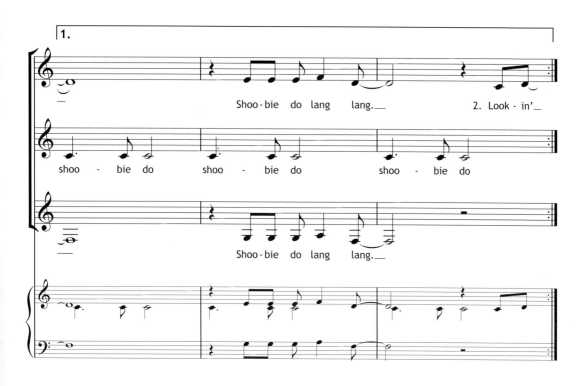

Shoo - bie do lang lang.___   2. Look - in'___

shoo - bie do   shoo - bie do   shoo - bie do

Shoo - bie do lang lang.___

D.S. al Coda

Coda

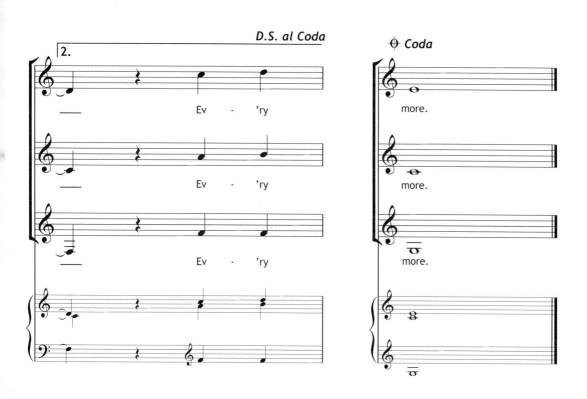

Ev - 'ry

Ev - 'ry

Ev - 'ry

more.

more.

more.

With A Little Help From My Friends

Words & Music by John Lennon & Paul McCartney

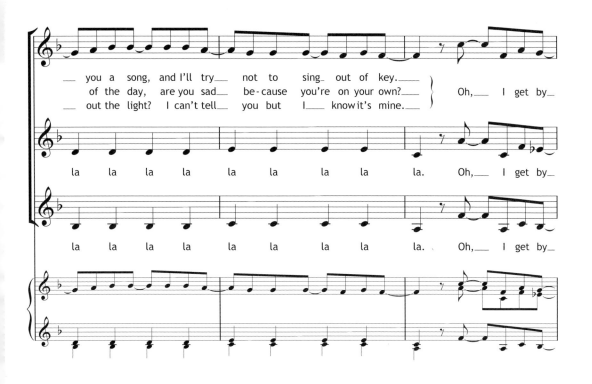

you a song, and I'll try__ not to sing__ out of key.__
of the day, are you sad__ be-cause you're on your own?__
out the light? I can't tell__ you but I__ know it's mine.__

Oh,__ I get by__

la la la la la la la la la. Oh,__ I get by__

la la la la la la la la la. Oh,__ I get by__

— with a lit-tle help__ from my friends.__ I get high__ with a lit-tle help__ from my friends,

— with a lit-tle help__ from my friends.__ I get high__ with a lit-tle help__ from my friends,

— with a lit-tle help__ from my friends.__ I get high__ with a lit-tle help__ from my friends,

I'm gon-na try___ with a lit-tle help from my friends.___

I'm gon-na try___ with a lit-tle help from my friends.___ La la la

I'm gon-na try___ with a lit-tle help from my friends.___ La la la

Do you need___ a - ny - bo - dy? I

Do do do do do do do do do do do

Do do do do do do do do do do do

54

need some - bo - dy to love.___ Could it be___ a - ny - bo-

need some - bo - dy to love.___ Do do do do do do do

need some - bo - dy to love.___ Do do do do do do do

To Coda ⊕   D.C. al Coda

- dy   I want some - bo - dy to love.

do do do do   want some - bo - dy to love.   Do do do.

do do do do   want some - bo - dy to love.   Do do do.

⊕ Coda

I get by___ with a lit-tle help___ from my friends,

I get by___ with a lit-tle help___ from my friends,

I get by___ with a lit-tle help___ from my friends,

___ with a lit-tle help___ from my friends.___

___ with a lit tle help___ from my friends.___

___ with a lit-tle help___ from my friends.___

4 5 6 7 8 9
8/10(175149)